BORING DETAILS

Scholastic Children's Books,
Scholastic Publications Ltd,
7-9 Pratt Street, London NW1 0AE, UK

Scholastic Inc.,
555 Broadway, New York, NY 10012-3999, USA

Scholastic Canada Ltd,
123 Newkirk Road, Richmond Hill,
Ontario, Canada, L4C 3G5

Ashton Scholastic Pty Ltd
PO Box 579, Gosford
New South Wales, Australia

Ashton Scholastic Ltd,
Private Bag 92801, Penrose, Auckland,
New Zealand

First published by Scholastic Publications Ltd, 1994

Copyright © Chris Winn (Holdings) Ltd, 1994.
Licensed by Copyright Promotions Ltd.

ISBN: 0 590 54182 X

Printed and bound in Hong Kong

10 9 8 7 6 5 4 3 2 1

All rights reserved

The right of Chris Winn to be identified as author of this work has been asserted
by him in accordance with the Copyright, Design and Patents Act, 1988.

This book is sold subject to the condition that it shall not, by way of
trade or otherwise be lent, resold, hired out, or otherwise circulated
without the publisher's prior consent in any form of binding or cover
other than that in which it is published and without a similar condition,
including this condition, being imposed upon the subsequent purchaser.

TO ALEX AND ROSIE

With thanks to everyone involved
in the production of this book,
and in particular to my brother
Richard Winn and to Andie Peck
for their great skill in helping to
complete the illustrations.

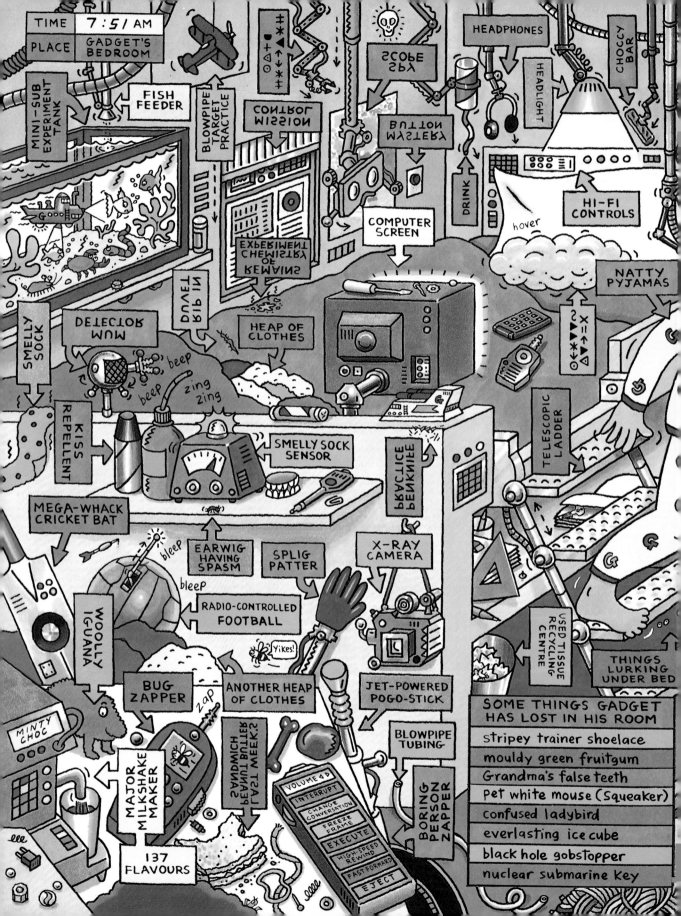

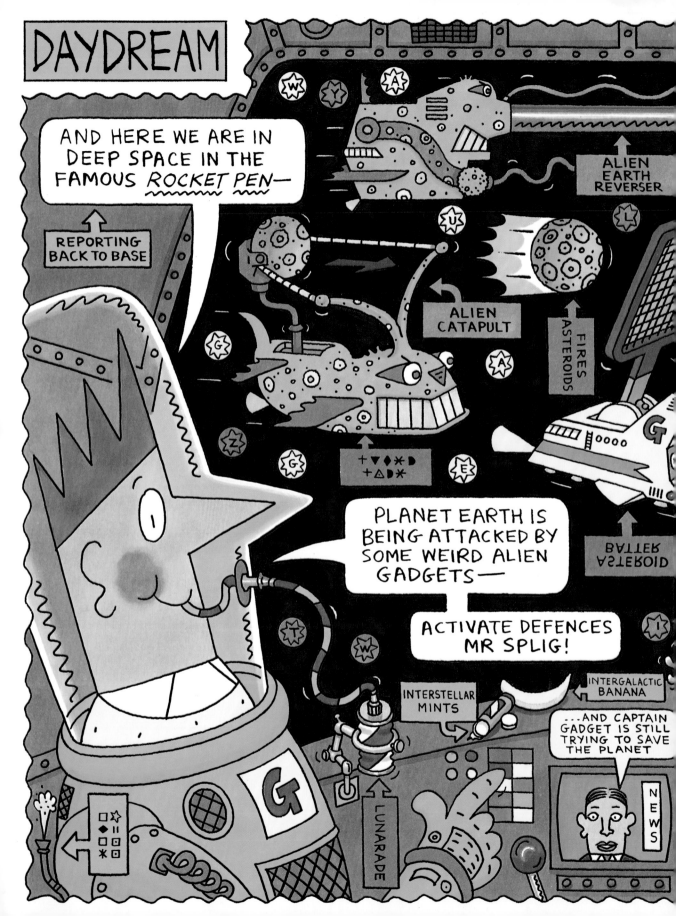

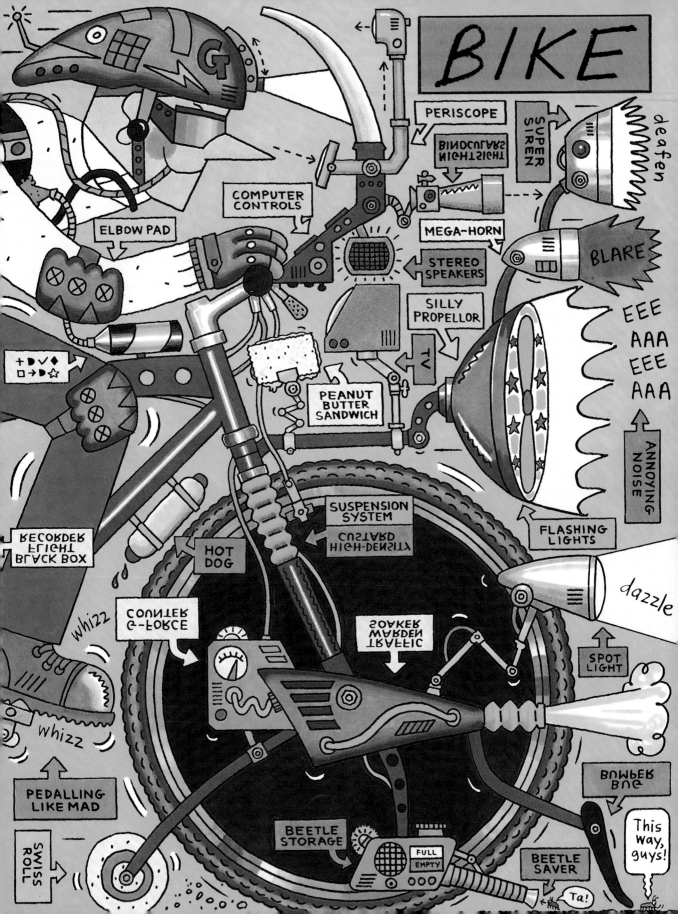

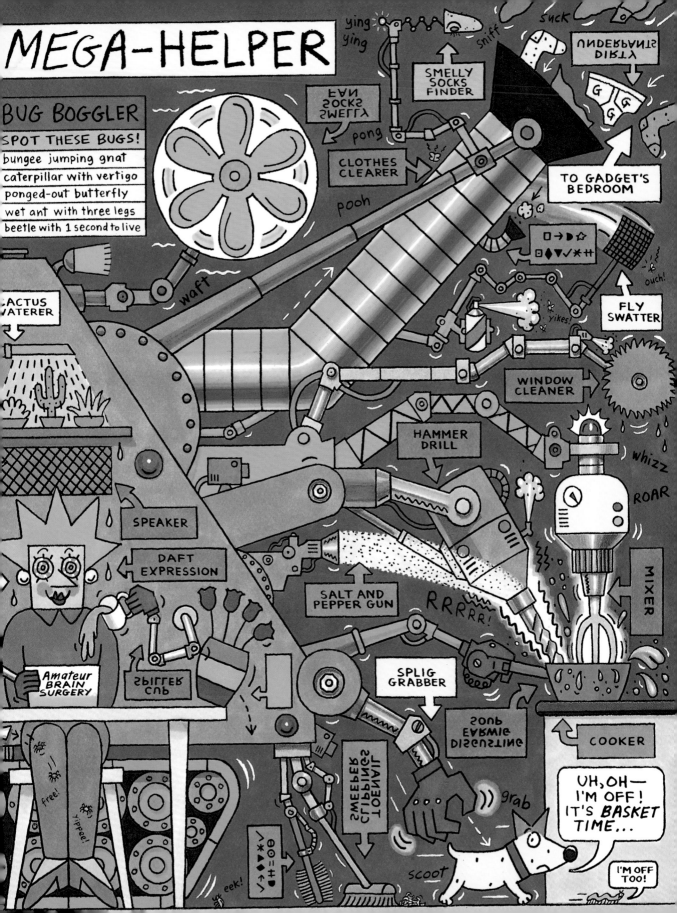